Seven is Heaven!

The Great Big Book for Seven-year-olds

Compiled by Treld Bicknell

COLLINS

Some Seven-ish Poems

Illustrated by Leon Baxter

What someone said when he was spanked on the day before his birthday

Some day
I may
Pack my bag and run away.
Some day
I may.
– But not today.

Some night
I might
Slip away in the moonlight.
I might.
Some night.
– But not tonight.

Some night.
Some day.
I might.
I may.
– But right now I think I'll stay.

John Ciardi

Miss T.

It's a very odd thing –
As odd as can be –
That whatever Miss T. eats
Turns into Miss T.;
Porridge and apples,
Mince, muffins and mutton,
Jam, junket, jumbles –
Not a rap, not a button
It matters; the moment
They're out of her plate,
Though shared by Miss Butcher
And sour Mr. Bate;
Tiny and cheerful,
And neat as can be,
Whatever Miss T. eats
Turns into Miss T.

Walter de la Mare

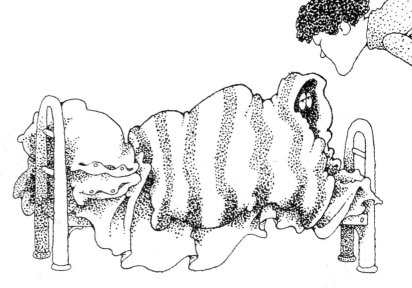

Lazy Lucy

Lazy Lucy
lay in bed.
Lazy Lucy's
mother said:
"You will drive
your mother crazy.
Upsy-daisy,
Lucy Lazy!"
To her mom
said Lazy Lucy,
"Little children
can't be choosy
(though I would
prefer to snooze
in my bed
if I could choose).
I will not
drive Mamma crazy,
I will not
at all be lazy,
I will jump
right out of bed
– and be Sleepy Lu
instead."

N. M. Bodecker

See what you can make

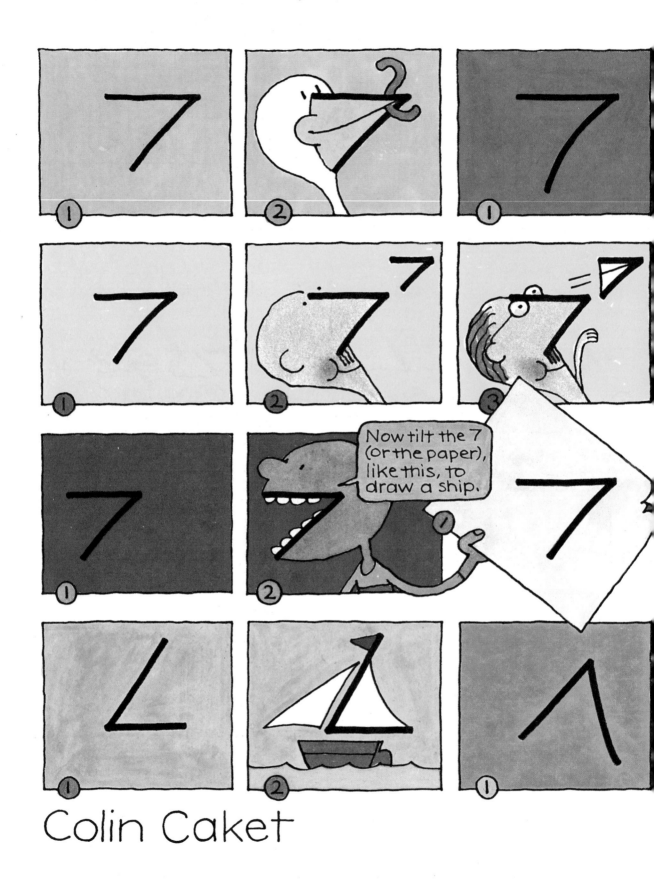

Colin Caket

The Seven Pile

by Peter Eldin
Illustrated by Kate Shannon

Seven is a very magical number. It is said to possess mystical powers because it was once believed that there were seven sacred planets, and because there are seven days in the week, and seven ages in the life of man.

Here's a bit of a mystery surrounding the number seven. Read the following rhyme – which is very old – and see if you can work out the answer in your head (and that means you must not cheat by using a computer or a calculator).

St Ives

As I was going to St Ives,
I met a man with seven wives,
Each wife had seven cats,
Each cat had seven kits,
How many were going
to St Ives?

In fact only the person saying the rhyme – "I" – is going to St Ives so the answer is one! If you add up all the other people in the rhyme, the man, his wives, their cats and the kittens the answer is 400, but they were coming *from* St Ives. (Incidentally, this is an old British riddle and there are, in fact, two places in Britain that are called St Ives – but no one seems to know *which* St Ives

is the one mentioned in the rhyme – so that is as much of a puzzle as the puzzle itself!)

*

The Seven Pile

Here is a magic trick you can try.

1. Take a pack of cards and remove the four sevens. Place them in a face-down pile on the table.

2. Now make a second pile of seven other cards. Put *them* face down on the table next to the first pile.

3. In a third face-down pile, put a four, a two and an ace.

4. On a piece of paper write, "You will choose the seven pile." Fold the paper in half and you are now ready to show someone the trick.

5. Point to the three piles of cards and ask a friend to pick any one of the piles. As soon as one pile is chosen pick up the other two piles and place them back in the pack.

6. Now ask your friend to open up the paper which has been resting on the table all the time. No matter *which* pile your friend chooses, the wording on the paper will be correct. If it is the first pile, it will be right because it is *all* sevens, the second pile consists of seven cards and the cards in the third pile add up to seven.

When you do this trick don't say *anything* about what is in each pile or your audience will soon guess how the trick was done.

*

Danny : I think my dog can do arithmetic.

Manny : What makes you think that?

Danny : When I asked him what seven minus seven was he said nothing.

Teacher : If you had seven cakes and someone asked you for one, how many would you have left?

Pupil : Seven.

*

How Many Words?

The seventh letter of the alphabet is G. How many words of four or more letters can you think of that begin with G? Make a list and see how many you get.

When you have made your list take a look in a dictionary. You will find that there are lots of words you forgot and lots, lots more that you've never come across before. *Gee!*

The Wolf and the Seven Little Goats

The Brothers Grimm ● Retold by Shirley Greenway
Illustrated by Susan Williams

Once there was an old mother goat who had seven little kids and she loved them all dearly. One day, before she went out to find them some food, she called her little kids to come to her.

"My children," she said, "I must go into the woods and fields today and, while I am gone, you must look out for the wolf. He will try to come into the house and, if ever he does, he will surely eat you all up, skin and bones and all.

He is so cunning that even the cleverest goat may be fooled by his disguises, but *you* will always find him out – for he cannot hide his hoarse voice and black paws."

"Do not be afraid, dear mother," answered the seven kids. "We will take good care *not* to let the wolf into the house." Comforted by these words, the mother goat went on her way, promising to be home before sunset. After a time the kids heard a voice at the door crying out: "Open the door, my dear children, your mother has come back, and I have brought good things to eat." But the kids recognized the wolf's hoarse voice and would not open the door.

"Go away!" they cried. "You are not our mother. Her voice is sweet and kind and yours is hoarse and cruel. We know you are the wolf."

Angrily, the wolf went away and, when he found a big lump of chalk, he ate it up to make his voice soft and sweet. Then he returned to the mother goat's house and knocked very softly at the door.

"Open the door, my dear children," he purred, "your mother is here with surprises for you." But, as he spoke, the wolf rested his black paws against the window ledge and the kids cried out: "We see your black paws and we know you are the wolf!"

The wolf then ran to the baker's shop and, stealthily opening the nearest sack, he covered his four black paws with soft, white flour.

Now the wolf went a *third* time to the door, saying in his sweetest voice: "Open the door, my dear children, your mother has brought you each something nice from the fields." And he put his paws up against the window and the kids saw that they were not black, and they opened the door! The wolf bounded into the house. Terrified, the seven little goats ran in every direction – trying to hide themselves. The first ran into the kitchen, the second got into bed, the third crouched beneath the table, the fourth scurried out into the yard, the fifth shut himself in the cupboard and the sixth dived under the sink. There was nowhere for the smallest to hide – so she squeezed herself into the grand-father clock that stood by the door – and huddled there without daring to breathe.

Meanwhile, the wolf rushed into every room, searching for the little goats in their hiding places. He popped each little goat in turn into a large sack which he found hanging in the cupboard where the fifth little goat was hiding. Then he hurried back to his lair dragging with him the sack filled with struggling little goats. But soon he felt tired and, hiding the sack behind some rocks, he lay down under a tree and went to sleep.

*

Soon after, the mother goat returned with food for her kids and found – Oh, such a terrible sight met her eyes! The door stood open, the tables and chairs lay tumbled about, the dishes broken and bedclothes torn from the bed. Worst of all, her children had vanished – in vain she bleated their names one by one. But as she called the name of the smallest kid, a little voice cried, "Here I am, mother, here in the clock-case." ▶

She let the smallest kid out and, when she heard that they had been tricked into letting the wolf into the house and that he had carried six of her kids away, she grew very angry. She set off down the path with the smallest kid running at her heels. She did not stop until she came to the spot where the wolf lay sleeping beneath the tree – dreaming of the good dinner he would soon have. He was snoring so loudly that the branches shook but – between the snores – the mother goat thought she heard another sound.

"Can it be," she thought, "that my dear children are still alive!"

Searching among the rocks she found the sack and heard the feeble cries of her kids coming from inside it. But, alas, the mouth of the sack was tightly secured and weighted down with a heavy stone which she could not move. She told the smallest kid to run quickly back home for some shears and a needle and thread. Then she whispered gently to her kids to be very still and she cut a long slit in the side of the sack. The six little goats leapt out onto the grass as well as ever they had been. They were overjoyed that their dear mother had found them. She told each one to go and find a round, hard stone. Then she quickly filled the

sack and neatly sewed up the slit in its side. The mother goat took her kids and hid behind the largest rocks.

At that moment the wolf awoke from his nap. So hungry was he, that he ran to his hiding place, snatched up the sack, opened it and swallowed its contents in six huge gulps. Almost at once he began to feel quite strange, and very thirsty, from his dusty dinner. But when he tried to walk to the brook to drink, the stones rattled and crashed one against the other. And he cried out:

What is this I feel inside me
knocking hard against my bones?
How should such a thing betide me!
They were kids and now they're stones.

At last he reached the brook and bent his head to drink, but the six hard stones inside him weighed him down. He toppled over into the water and was carried rapidly downstream by the swift-running little brook.

The wolf was heard of no more – and never again were little goats tricked into opening their door by a wicked wolf with a hoarse voice and four black paws. ✳

Matchmakers

devised by Titus Bicknell
Illustrated by Naomi Games

How many different things can you make from just seven matchsticks?

Here's an easy one for you to try.

How about this?

Make seven from eight by taking away four.

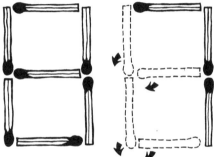

Here are seven more.

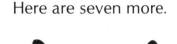

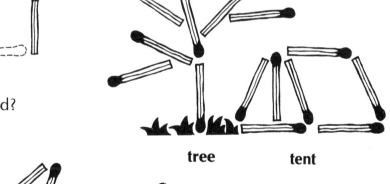

tree   tent

Well, how many did you find?

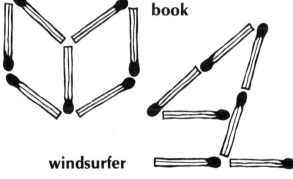

book

windsurfer

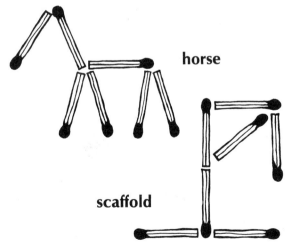

horse

scaffold

bridge

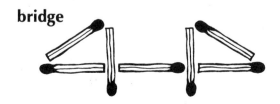

the MAGNIFICENT SEVEN

adapted and drawn by Peter Wingham

A little Mexican village.

The ALARM bell!

BANDITOS!

Run for your LIVES!

Hide the SWEETS!

HELP!

They've stolen EVERYTHING!

The CREEPS!

We'll be BACK!

YAHOOOO!

YIPEE!

We can't go on like this! What are we to do?

Pedro! You must ride to the town for help!

There's the town. Now to find some help.

In the saloon.

Our little village needs help to fight some BANDITOS!

I will!

Me too!

And me!

ICES

SNAP!

Who will ride back with me?

Ready when you are!

I'll come!

Count me in!

Splendid Septenaries: *The Magical Mystical Seven* ✳ ## by Felicity Trotman

Once upon a time . . . there was a young man who was given a pair of seven-league boots . . . Have *you* ever dreamed of finding a pair of seven-league boots, which would carry you twenty-one miles with every stride? Or imagined signing on as a cabin-boy on a pirate ship, and going off to sail the Seven Seas? Have you ever been so happy and excited about something that you could describe yourself as being in seventh heaven?

From the very earliest times, seven has been a most important number. Wise men in the ancient world believed that the number three represented Heaven and the soul, and four represented the Earth and the body. The two added together make seven, and that represented the Universe, perfection, safety, plenty, completeness.

For that reason, seven has always been regarded as a special, usually lucky, number. Groups of seven things are particularly interesting, like the seven days in a week and the seven colours in the rainbow.

Ancient Egyptians knew of the seven wise hawks of Ra, their sun-god, and the seven fates of the goddess Hathor. There were seven houses of the Underworld, with three times seven gates and the number seven itself was sacred to the god, Osiris. The Greeks thought the number was sacred to Apollo, who had seven strings on his lyre. Pan played seven pipes. These ideas were borrowed by the Romans. Rome itself is built on seven hills, though some of them are rather difficult to find now because they are so covered in buildings!

All the major religions in the world have special sevens.

For Jewish people, there are seven great holy days in the year. The great candlestick, the Menorah, has seven branches, Solomon's Temple in Jerusalem took seven years to build and there are Seven Pillars of Wisdom. The Hebrew verb for swearing an oath actually means "to come under the influence of seven things"

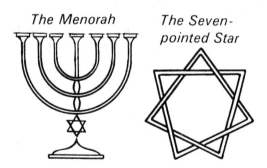

The Menorah *The Seven-pointed Star*

Jews and Christians together share the Old Testament where many sevens are found. God took seven days to make the world and everything in it. Joshua and the men of Israel marched round Jericho seven times on the seventh day, led by seven priests blowing seven ram's-horn trumpets before the walls came tumbling down. The leper,

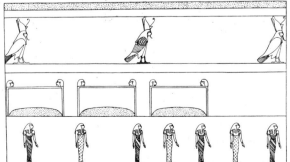

The Seventh Hour of the night

Naaman, was commanded to bathe seven times in the waters of Jordan to cure his dreadful disease and, when the prophet, Elisha, raised a child from the dead, the boy sneezed seven times as he came back to life. In the story of the Flood, Noah sent his dove out seven days after he sent out the raven — and it was seven months after the beginning of the Flood that the Ark came to rest.

The Seven Spirits

Also in the Bible, the Book of Revelation tells us that there were seven churches in Asia, and in his great vision St John saw seven candlesticks, seven stars, seven trumpets, seven spirits before the throne of God, seven horns, seven plagues, a seven-headed monster and the Lamb with seven eyes.

Hindus have some interesting sevens, too. There are seven gods before the flood in their story, and seven wise men saved from it. There are also seven jewels of the Brahmanas.

Moslems regard seven as the perfect number. They also count seven heavens, seven earths and seven seas. They have seven prophets, and the Ka'aba, the sacred building in Mecca, is walked round seven times, representing the seven attributes of God. And in Japan, there are seven gods of luck.

Thomas the Rhymer leaves his Fairy Queen

Magic was sometimes part of religion, and was also an early form of science. There were seven knots in a cord for spellbinding, and seven-fold incantations. Alchemists, trying to turn base metals into gold, used seven metals, each related to seven planets. Each planet in turn was thought to have its own heaven, and from that sprang a belief that man had seven senses.

In the Middle Ages, people enjoyed stories about the Seven Champions — the patron saints of England, Scotland, Wales, Ireland, France, Spain and Italy.

There was another famous story about the Seven Sleepers — seven young men from Ephesus who were Christian. In the year 250 AD there was a persecution of Christians, and to escape, they hid in a cave. Here they fell asleep — and did not wake up for 230 years, by which time they were quite safe! Ogier the Dane, hero of many medieval stories, thunders on the floor with his mace once every seven years, and Thomas the Rhymer spent seven years underground, enchanted by the queen of Fairyland.

Another famous old story tells of the Seven against Thebes — the heroes of ancient Greece, seven in number, who fought to restore the rightful king of Thebes against his usurping uncle.

But that is probably enough sevens! No one can doubt that it is a splendid and important number, for wherever you look, in all parts of the world and at all times in history it has taken a prominent place. Lucky seven! ✳

Now You're Seven!
by Susan Foster

Illustrated by Kieron Glennon, Layla Branicki, Faye Reason and Glenn Bowman-Kearns

The pictures on these pages are the work of boys and girls who have had their seventh birthday. The children thought about what it is like to be seven years old. They realized that they were able to do many more things than they could when they were younger. Here are some of their ideas.

When you are **7** you feel older,

you can tell the time,

you can tie your shoe laces,

you are braver because you don't always cry when you are hurt,

you can help in the house,

you can roller skate or ride a bicycle really well,

you have masses of energy,

you can stay up later,

you can wash and dry yourself properly,

you can read books and you can learn to read music too.

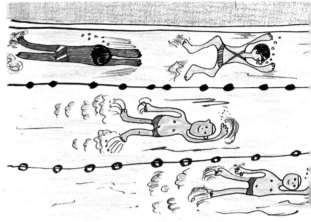

Growing up

Your life began when you were a baby. You learned to walk and to talk. You explored the world in and around your home, but you could not manage to do things for yourself. You spent a great deal of your time eating and sleeping. You were also very interested in yourself.

Now that you are older you can do many things without help. You have come to realize that other people are important and you enjoy the company of friends and relations. You let children join in your games and play with your toys. By the time you are seven years old you are used to going to school. When you were younger, school was very strange and new. Now you can read and write, isn't that great? You can also compute numbers, question how some things work and why other things grow. You can experiment with arts and crafts and perhaps learn to play a musical instrument.

*

As you keep on growing, what changes can you expect? There are four different

kinds of change. The proper names for these changes are: physical development (all about your body); mental development (all about your mind); social development (learning about living); emotional development (all about your feelings).

Your body

Your body is growing very fast. You are taller, bigger, and stronger. Because of these things you can do physical things like running, jumping, swimming, climbing, or cycling really well.

Your mind

Your brain is like a computer which controls your thinking. Now you are able to work out problems by thinking, reading, and planning. Your brain needs to be used so don't let other people do all your thinking for you.

Your friends

Everybody likes to have friends. At home and at school you share your life with other people and maybe you could join a club. Then you would meet other children. It is very important for you to be happy with many different people.

Your feelings

Your own feelings are a very special part of you. Nobody can know *exactly* how you feel, but people may get an idea by the way you behave. It is easy to see when somebody is happy or excited. You will know, too, when a person is sad or miserable. There are so many different feelings for you to experience. Learning about love, friendship, anger, fear, or disappointment is all part of growing up.

Now that you are seven you can't stop there! You will go on developing year after year until you are an adult. Before your next birthday, see if you can learn to do something really new. *

A Good Read

Here are books to read – and read again – chosen by **Elaine Moss** *from* THE GOOD BOOK GUIDE TO CHILDREN'S BOOKS.

A Bear Called Paddington

by Michael Bond
Illustrated by Peggy Fortnum

Stories about Paddington Bear's attempts to be helpful – which always end in disaster.

James and the Giant Peach

by Roald Dahl
Illustrated by Nancy Ekholm Burkert

Dahl's first book for children is, in many ways, his best. James escapes from his cruel aunts through a tunnel that leads to the centre of a huge peach – which rolls downhill and squashes them. His peach adventure, with enlarged insects, threatening sharks, and co-operative seagulls, have the grace, humour and fantasy of a latter-day "Alice."

Arabel's Raven

by Jeff Brown
Illustrated by Tomi Ungerer

To most of the Jones family the raven (found in the fridge drinking milk and pecking at sausages) is a nuisance. But Arabel gives him a name, Mortimer, and he becomes a resourceful and off-beat friend. Hilarious.

Flat Stanley

by Jeff Brown
Illustrated by Tomi Ungerer

Stanley Lambchop is squashed flat by a noticeboard that falls on him. It's fun – *at first* – to be flown like a kite but the "flat" adventures quickly pall and he is thrilled to be reinflated by his brother.

Charlotte's Web

by E.B. White
Illustrated by Garth Williams

Fern, the farmer's daughter, and all the animals and insects of goodwill on the farm unite to save Wilbur the pig from slaughter. Charlotte the spider's plan is the most ingenious, and through it Wilbur is saved.

Adventures of the Little Wooden Horse

by Ursula Moray Williams

No-one buys the Little Wooden Horse that the old toymaker has carved – so the Little Wooden Horse goes out into the cruel world to earn money to repay his master. One of the saddest – and loveliest – stories ever written.

The Iron Man

by Ted Hughes
Illustrated by Andrew Davidson

Hughes holds readers wide-eyed with this short, spare tale of a gigantic iron-eating robot that appears from nowhere and frightens all the villagers but young Hogarth, an observant boy who understands the Iron Man's needs. Is the Iron Man a threat, or will he protect the world against a fearful amorphous terror from Outer Space? A thrilling, suspenseful tale told by a poet.

Finn Family Moomintroll

by Tove Jansson

Far away in Finland live the Moomins, a family just like any other – except that they hibernate under the winter snow, look like little horse trolls, and they and their friends have wonderful names like Snufkin, Hemulen and the Snork Maiden.

One Hundred and One Dalmatians

by Dodie Smith

Imagine the consternation of Pongo and Missis, parent Dalmatians, when their fifteen pups are stolen by the unspeakable Cruella de Vil so that she can make coats and gloves from their spotted skins! The parents, helped by messages through a network of dogs known as the Twilight Barking, set out on a dangerous, adventurous rescue mission. Thrilling, sad, funny.

Little House on the Prairie
by Laura Ingalls Wilder

The most popular of the Little House books, this one tells how Laura's family moved from the "Big Woods" in their covered wagon and travelled West (with the frontier) to the Prairie. Adventure all the way, but the enduring quality of these marvellous books is the feeling that home is where your family is – even if bears and unfriendly Indians are on the prowl outside.

*

The Fairy Stories of Oscar Wilde
Illustrated by Harold Jones

Wilde's haunting fairy stories, sad, romantic, philosophical, rank with the great traditional tales that stir children's imaginations. Included are The Happy Prince, The Young King, and The Selfish Giant.

Five Children Stories
by E. Nesbit

The magic that transforms the urban world of the five children into another time, another place, is first the Psammead, a Sand Fairy, then an amulet with ancient Egyptian connections, and finally a Phoenix that has strange powers over an apparently unremarkable second-hand carpet. *Five Children and It, The Story of the Amulet,* and *The Phoenix and the Carpet.*

Just So Stories
by Rudyard Kipling

The large, complete edition, with big type and Kipling's own illustrations of How the Alphabet Became, The Elephant's Child and The Cat that Walked by Himself, is the best edition for enjoying the full range of Kipling's genius.

Simon and the Witch
by Margaret Stuart Barry
Illustrated by Linda Birch

Simon's best friend is a witch. Not any ordinary witch – but she can do some magic (just about). Lovely adventures for Simon, the Witch and her TV mad cat, George.

You Can't Catch Me!
by Michael Rosen
Illustrated by Quentin Blake

Some of Michael Rosen's best poems for young children – on being the youngest, on dogs, on being afraid of the dark – with lively watercolour illustrations for the listener to look at.

A Child's Garden of Verses
by Robert Louis Stevenson
Illustrated by Erik Blegvad

Evocative of a past way of life with Nursie, lamplighters and lead soldiers. Robert Louis Stevenson's poems, so rich in child vision, have a lasting appeal. This edition has the additional magic of Erik Blegvad's glorious illustrations in full colour.

The Birthday Party Chase
by Jane Bottomley

Help seven friends make their way to the birthday party in the forest.

Choose a coloured button or counter and decide which of the animals you're going to be. Then, take turns throwing the dice. Make your way – carefully – along the forest track. But watch out for danger – you might fall into the stream or meet a fox!

If you land on an orange or yellow square, obey the instructions and either move on or go back to the appropriately numbered square. Have fun! ▶

74

75

76

77

Welcome to the Party!

62

61

60

59

hear music
hurry on four

58

57

wobble off wall
to 53

56

47

55

48 climb up
to 60

49

50

51

watch out for
Willy Weasel!
run back to 32

54

52

53

37

36

skip along
branch to 45

35

34

33

32

31

27

28

run along
branch to 33

29

30
faced by
fox --back
to 27

15

14

13

12

11

scamper
over to 16

10

cuttle
p hollow
ee to 50

5

6

7

hop across
to 13

8

dilly dally by the
water – miss a go

9

Making Presents
by Deborah Manley
Illustrated by Charlotte Knox

Here are some things that you can make for your friends and family — whatever their ages — to enjoy throughout the year.

*

A Noticeboard

Everyone has bits and pieces they want to keep: postcards, sports programmes, pictures of rock stars and friends, badges, certificates for swimming or good work at school . . . You can make a noticeboard for a friend where they can display all these souvenirs.

You need:

a sheet of strong card or light board
adhesive paper (like shelf-lining paper), cloth or other material — a few centimetres larger than the board all around
narrow elastic (which comes on cards of about 3 metres), bias binding tape or decorated ribbon — all in bright colours
drawing pins or staples
glue, scissors and string

How to make it

1. Fix the cloth carefully on the board, lapping it over the edges. It will be easier to do this if you *can* use adhesive-backed material. Other materials can be glued down.

2. Crisscross lengths of the elastic (tape or ribbon) over the board as shown, fixing them firmly on the back with drawing pins or staples.

3. Fix a loop of string to the back of the board to hang it by.

4. Put a birthday or gift card on the board, so your friend knows how to use it.

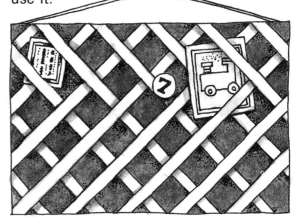

Peppermint Creams
Some sweets in a pretty box make a lovely present and these are very easy to make because they need hardly any cooking.

You need:

$1\frac{1}{2}$ cups caster sugar
$\frac{1}{2}$ tablespoon melted butter
2 tablespoons full cream milk
3 drops peppermint flavouring
a drop or two of food colouring
a little icing sugar

How to make them

1. Warm the milk and pour it into a mixing bowl.

2. Stir in the melted butter, sugar, and peppermint flavouring and mix it well.

3. Divide the mixture into two. Leave one part white; mix a drop of food colouring well into the other part.

4. Knead the two lots of mixture with your hands until each is well mixed and smooth.

5. Dust a pastry board with icing sugar. Pat or roll out the mixture until it is about 5mm thick.

6. Cut into shapes with a small cutter — you could use an egg cup.

Put the peppermint creams into a pretty box, or little basket, lined with coloured paper or a paper doily. Cover them over with cling film and tie the box with a colourful ribbon.

Sugar Mice

You can make these with the same mixture as you use for peppermint creams — leaving out the peppermint flavouring and colouring half the mixture pink.

How to make them

Shape the mixture into mice; some can be big, grown-up mice and some can be tiny, baby mice.

Mark the eyes. Fix on whiskers, made of thread, and string tails by pushing the ends into the body and smoothing them over.

You could make a little nest of soft paper in a basket for the mice to travel in.

A Pencil Holder

This makes a very useful present for someone's desk, either at work or at home, or in the kitchen by the telephone so there's always a pen handy.

You need:

a soup tin (opened with a wall tin opener so there is no jagged edge — get someone to help you with the opening)
some oil-based paint or enamel
a paint brush
a piece of adhesive shelf-paper, plastic or felt
glue and scissors

How to make it

1. Remove the label from the tin. Wash and dry it well.

2. Paint the inside of the tin. (Don't use *too* much paint or it will run down the tin in rivulets and blobs – take it slowly and brush it on as evenly as you can.)

3. Cut a piece of the adhesive material you've chosen large enough to go round the tin with a small overlap.

4. Lay the tin carefully in the centre of the *adhesive side* (or, if you are using felt or other non-adhesive material, the side on which you have *carefully* applied the glue) of the material. Wrap the material firmly and smoothly around the tin sticking down the overlapping seam.

If your covering material is a plain colour, you can decorate it with strips of cloth, flowers, sequins or badges to make it more personal. Then you can put a few pencils, felt-tip pens, and ball point pens into the pencil holder to complete your present.

Decorated Eggs

For centuries, giving decorated eggs has been a symbol of the coming of spring. In Russia a famous jeweller, called Fabergé, used to make beautiful eggs of gold, silver, and precious jewels for wealthy people to give as presents.

You can make painted and even "jewelled" eggs, too, to give at Easter time or to welcome the spring.

You need: gold or silver thread
little glass beads, sequins, and scraps of lace
a good clean clear adhesive

2 eggs
a large needle
felt-tip pens
clear nail varnish

How to make them

To blow an egg:

1. Keep the egg at room temperature overnight.

2. Holding the egg very carefully, pierce it at either end with your needle. Make the hole at the *wider end* larger by working it round with the needle.

3. If your needle is long enough, try to pierce through the yolk of the egg. Shake the egg to mix it up inside.

4. Hold the egg over a bowl and blow gently through the *smaller hole* until the contents of the egg come out of the larger hole and drop into the bowl.

5. Rinse out the empty egg shell with cold water. Stand it in an egg cup or in an egg box so all the water drains out.

Now your egg is ready to decorate.

For a painted egg:

1. Plan your decoration on a piece of paper first, or draw it onto the shell very lightly with a pencil. Then decorate the egg with your felt-tip pens.
2. When the decoration has dried, paint it over with clear nail varnish. To do this, hold the egg at one end and varnish the other. Let it dry, then turn it over and varnish the other end. The varnish will make the egg bright and shiny.

For a jewelled egg:

1. Paint a blown egg all over in one colour and varnish it.

2. Trace out your pattern on the shell in pencil.

3. Use a natchstick to put little dabs of glue where you want your "jewels" to go. Lick your finger and then pick up the beads and sequins and put them in position.

Patchwork Cushion Cover

You can make a very attractive cushion cover from quite small bits of cloth.

You need:

a square of plain cotton cloth, about 30 cm square for the back
16 pieces of cotton — some plain and some patterned — each about 9 cm square
a needle and thread

How to make it

1. Plan the patchwork side of your cushion cover so that you get a checker board effect of plain and patterned squares.

2. Sew the pieces of each line of *four* squares together with a simple back stitch. *Very carefully* press the seams flat.

3. Sew the *four* rows of squares together. Again press the seams flat (putting the iron back on to its rest each time!).

4. Lay the patchwork *face down* against the piece of plain cloth for the back. Sew the two pieces together on *three* sides.

5. Turn the cover right side out and press it neatly. Your cushion cover is ready. *

Septimus Septimusson

by E. Nesbit
Illustrated by Chris Molan

E. Nesbit is probably best known for her story of The Railway Children, *but she also wrote many wonderful shorter tales — among them this story of Septimus, the seventh son of a seventh son who went out to seek his fortune.*

*

The wind was screaming over the marsh. It shook the shutters and rattled the windows, and the little boy lay awake in the bare attic. His mother came softly up the ladder stairs, shading the flame of the tallow candle with her hand.

"I'm not asleep, Mother," said he. And she heard the tears in his voice.

"Why, silly lad," she said, sitting down on the straw-bed beside him and putting the candle on the floor. "What are you crying for?"

"It's the wind keeps calling me, Mother," he said. "It won't let me alone. It never has since I put up the little weathercock for it to play with. It keeps saying: 'Wake up, Septimus Septimusson, wake up, you're the seventh son of a seventh son. You can see the fairies and hear the beasts speak, and you must go out and seek your fortune.' And I'm afraid, and I don't want to go."

"I should think not, indeed," said his mother. "The wind doesn't talk, Sep, not really. You just go to sleep like a good boy, and I'll get Father to bring you a gingerbread pig from the fair tomorrow."

But Sep lay awake a long time listening to what the wind really did keep on saying, and feeling ashamed to think how frightened he was of going out all alone to seek his fortune – a thing all the boys in books were only too happy to do.

Next evening, father brought home the loveliest gingerbread pig with currant eyes. Sep ate it, and it made him less anxious than ever to go out into the world, where, perhaps, no one would give him gingerbread pigs ever any more.

Before he went to bed, he ran down to the shore where a great new harbour was being made. The workmen had been blasting the big rocks, and on one of the rocks a lot of mussels were sticking. He stood looking at them, and then suddenly he heard a lot of little voices crying: "Oh, Sep, we're so frightened, we're choking."

The voices were thin and sharp as the edges of mussel shells. They were, indeed, the voices of the mussels themselves.

"Oh, dear," said Sep, "I'm so sorry, but I can't move the rock back into the sea, you know. Can I now?"

"No," said the mussels, "but if you speak to the wind – you know his language and he's very fond of you since you made that toy for him – he'll blow the sea up till the waves wash us back into deep water."

"But I'm afraid of the wind," said Sep, "it says things that frighten me."

"Oh, very well," said the mussels, "we don't want you to be afraid. We can die all right if necessary."

Then Sep shivered and trembled.

"Go away," said the thin sharp voices. "We'll die – but we'd rather die in our own brave company."

"I know I'm a coward," said Sep. "Oh, wait a minute."

"Death won't wait," said the little voices.

"I can't speak to the wind, I won't," said Sep, and almost at the same moment he heard himself call out: "Oh, wind, please come and blow up the waves to save the poor mussels."

The wind answered with a boisterous shout: "All right, my boy," it shrieked, "I'm coming." And come it did. And when it had attended to the mussels, it came and whispered to Sep in his attic. And to his great surprise – instead of covering his head with the bedclothes as usual and trying not to listen – he found himself sitting up in bed and talking to the wind, man to man.

"Why," he said, "I'm not afraid of you any more."

"Of course not, we're friends now," said the wind. "That's because we joined together to do a kindness to someone. There's nothing like that for making people friends."

"Oh," said Sep.

"Yes," said the wind, "and now, when will you go out and seek your fortune? Remember how poor your father is, and the fortune – if you find it – won't be just for you, but for your father and mother and the others."

"Oh," said Sep, "I didn't think of that!"

"Yes," said the wind. "I do hate to bother you, but it's better to fix a time. Now when shall we start?"

"We?" said Sep. "Are you going with me?"

"I'll see you a bit of the way," said the wind. "What do you say now? Shall we start tonight? There's no time like the present."

"I do hate going," said Sep.

"Of course you do!" said the wind, cordially. "Come along. Get dressed and we'll make a beginning."

So Sep dressed and then he wrote on his slate in very big letters, "Gone to seek our fortune," and he put it on the ▶

29

table so that his mother should see it when she came down in the morning. And he went out of the cottage and the wind kindly shut the door after him.

The wind gently pushed him down to the shore, and there he got into his father's boat, which was called the *Septimus and Susie*, after his father and mother, and the wind carried him across to another country and there he landed.

"Now," said the wind, clapping him on the back, "off you go, and good luck to you!"

And it turned round and took the boat home again.

When Sep's mother found the writing on the slate, and his father found the boat gone, they feared that Sep was drowned, but when the wind brought the boat back wrong way up they were quite sure, and they both cried for many a long day.

The wind tried to tell them that Sep was all right, but they could not understand wind-talk, and they only said: "Blast the wind," and fastened the shutters up tight and put wedges in the windows.

Sep walked along the straight white road that led across the new country. He had no more idea how to look for *his* fortune than you would have if you suddenly stopped reading this and went out your front door to seek *yours*.

However, he had made a start, and

that is always something. When he had gone exactly seven miles on that straight foreign road, between strange trees and edged with flowers he did not know the names of, he heard a groaning in the wood and someone sighing and saying: "Oh, how hard it is, to have to die and never see my wife and the little cubs again."

The voice was rough as a lion's mane and strong as a lion's claws, and Sep was very frightened. But he said: "I'm not afraid," and then, oddly enough, he found he had spoken the truth – he wasn't afraid.

He broke through the bushes and found that the person who had spoken was indeed a lion. A lance had pierced its shoulder and fastened it to a great tree.

"All right," cried Sep. "Hold still a minute, sir."

He got out his knife and cut and cut at the shaft of the lance until he was able to break it off. Then the lion drew back and the broken shaft passed cleanly through the wound.

"I'm really extremely obliged, my dear fellow," said the lion, warmly. "Pray command me, if there is any little thing I can do for you at any time."

"Don't mention it," said Sep, with equal politeness. "Delighted to have been of use to you, I'm sure."

So they parted. As Sep scrambled through the bushes back to the road, he kicked against an axe that lay on the ground.

"Hello," said he, "some poor woodman's dropped this, and not been able to find it! I'll take it along – perhaps I may meet him."

He was getting very tired and very hungry and he sat down to rest under a chestnut tree. He heard two little voices talking in the branches, voices soft as a squirrel's fur and bright as a squirrel's eyes. They were, indeed, the voices of two squirrels.

"Hush," said one, "there's someone below."

"It's a horrid boy! Let's scurry away," said the other.

"I'm not a horrid boy," said Sep. "I'm the seventh son of a seventh son."

"Ah," said Mrs Squirrel, "of course, *that* makes all the difference! Have some nuts?"

"Oh, yes!" said Sep. "At least I mean, yes, if you please."

So the squirrels brought nuts down to him, and, when he had eaten as many as he wanted, they filled his pockets, and then in return he chopped all the lower boughs off the chestnut tree, so ▶

"Heavy, isn't it?" said the old gentleman.

"Yes," said Sep.

"Then I'll carry it for you," said the old gentleman. "For it's one that my head forester lost yesterday. And now come along with me, for you're the boy I've been looking for for seven years – an honest boy and the seventh son of a seventh son."

So Sep went home with the gentleman – who was a great lord in that country – and he lived in that lord's castle and was taught everything that a gentleman ought to know. And in return he told the lord all about the ways of birds and beasts – for as he understood their talk, he knew more about them than anyone else in that country. And the lord wrote it all down in a book, and half the people said it was wonderfully clever, and the other half said it was nonsense, and how could he know. That was fame, and the lord was very pleased. But although the old lord was so famous, he would not leave his castle, for he had a hump that an enchanter had fastened on to him, and he couldn't bear to be seen with it.

"But you'll get rid of it for me some day, my boy," he used to say. "No one but the seventh son of a seventh son and an honest boy can do it."

that boys who were *not* seventh sons could not climb up and interfere with the squirrels' housekeeping arrangements.

Then they parted – the best of friends – and Sep went on.

"I haven't found my fortune yet," he said. "But I've made a friend or two."

And just as he was saying that, he turned a corner of the road and met an old gentleman in a fur-lined coat riding a fine, big, grey horse.

"Hello!" said the gentleman. "Who are you, and where are you off to so bright and early?"

"I'm Septimus Septimusson," said Sep. "And I'm going to seek my fortune."

"And you've taken an axe to help you carve your way to glory?"

"No," said Sep, "I found it, and I suppose someone lost it. So I'm bringing it along in case I meet him."

So Sep grew up. And when he was twenty-one – straight as a lance and handsome as a picture – the old lord said to him:

"My boy, you've been like a son to me, but now it is time you got married and had sons of your own. Is there any girl you'd like to marry?"

"No," said Sep. "I never did care much for girls."

The old lord laughed.

"Then you must set out again and seek your fortune once more," he said. "Because no man has really found his fortune till he's found the one who is his heart's lady. Choose the best horse in the stable and off you go, lad, and my blessing go with you."

So Sep chose a good red horse and set out, and he rode straight to the great city that shone golden across the plain, and when he got there he found everyone crying.

"What is the matter?" said Sep, reining in the red horse in front of a smithy, where the apprentices were crying on to the fires and the smith was dropping tears on the anvil.

"Why, the Princess is dying," said the blacksmith, blowing his nose. "A nasty, wicked magician – he had a spite against the King, and he got at the Princess when she was playing ball in the garden, and now she's blind and deaf and dumb. And she won't eat."

"And she'll die," said the first apprentice.

"And she *is* such a dear," said the other apprentice.

Sep sat still on the red horse, thinking.

"Has anything been done?" he asked.

"Oh, yes," said the blacksmith. "All the doctors have seen her, but they can't do anything. And the King has advertised in the usual way, that anyone who can cure her may marry her. But it's no good. Kings' sons aren't what they used to be. A silly lot they are nowadays, all taken up with football and horse racing and golf."

"Humph," said Sep. "Thank you. Which is the way to the palace?"

The blacksmith pointed, and then burst into tears again. Sep rode on.

When he got to the palace, he asked to see the King. Everyone there was crying, too, from the footman who opened the door to the King, who was sitting upon his golden throne and looking at his fine collection of butterflies through floods of tears.

"Oh, dear me, yes, young man," said the King. "You may *see* her and welcome, but it's no good."

'We can but try," said Sep. So he was taken to the room where the Princess sat huddled up on her silver throne among the white velvet cushions, with her crown all on one side, crying out of her poor blind eyes, so that the tears ran down over her green gown with the red roses on it. ▶

And as soon as he saw her, Sep knew that she was the only girl – princess as she was, with a crown and a throne – who could ever be his heart's lady. He went up to her and kneeled at her side and took her hand and kissed it. The Princess started. She could not see or hear him, but at the touch of his hand and his lips, she knew that *he* was *her* heart's lord. She threw her arms around his neck and cried more than ever.

He held her in his arms and stroked her hair until she stopped crying, and then he called for bread and milk. This was brought in a silver basin, and he fed her as you feed a little child.

The news ran through the city: "The Princess has eaten," and all the bells were set ringing. Sep said goodnight to his Princess and went to bed in the best bedroom of the palace. Early in the grey morning, he got up and leaned out of the open window and called to his old friend the wind.

And the wind came bustling in and clapped him on the back, crying: "Well, my boy, and what can I do for you, eh?"

Sep told him about the Princess.

"Well," said the wind, "you've not done so badly. At any rate, you've got her love. And you couldn't have got that with anybody's help but your own. Now, of course, the thing to do is to find the wicked Magician."

"Of course," said Sep.

"Well – I travel a good deal – I'll keep my eyes open, and let you know if I hear anything."

Sep spent the day holding the Princess's hand and feeding her at meal times. That night the wind rattled his window and said: "Let me in."

It came in very noisily and said. "Well, I've found your Magician. He's in the forest pretending to be a mole."

"How can I find him?" said Sep.

"Haven't you any friends in the forest?" asked the wind.

Then Sep remembered his friends the squirrels, and he mounted his horse and rode away to the chestnut tree where they lived. They were charmed to see him grown so tall and strong and handsome, and when he had told them his story they said at once: "Oh, yes! Delighted to be of any service to you." And they called to all their brothers and cousins and uncles and nephews, to search the forest for a mole that wasn't really a mole. Quite soon they found him, and hustled and shoved him along until he was face to face with Sep. The glade was green, but all the bushes and trees around were red-brown with squirrel fur and shining bright with squirrel eyes.

Then Sep said: "Give the Princess back her eyes and her hearing and her voice." But the mole would not.

"Give the Princess back her eyes and her hearing and her voice," said Sep again. But the mole only gnashed his wicked teeth and snarled.

And then in a minute the squirrels fell on the mole and killed it, and Sep thanked them and rode back to the palace, for, of course, he knew that when a magician is killed, all his magic un-works itself instantly.

But when he got to his Princess, she was still as deaf as a post and as dumb as a stone, and she was still crying bitterly with her poor blind eyes. ▶

"Cheer up, my sweetheart," he said, though he knew she couldn't hear him, and as he spoke the wind came in at the open window and spoke very softly, because it was in the presence of the Princess.

"All right," it whispered, "the old villain gave us the slip that journey. Got out of the moleskin in the very nick of time. He's a wild boar now."

"Come," said Sep, fingering his sword-hilt, "I'll kill that myself, without asking it any questions."

So he went and fought it. But it was a most uncommon boar, as big as a horse, with tusks half a yard long; and although Sep wounded it, it jerked the sword out of his hand with its tusk, and was just going to trample on him when a great roar sounded through the forest.

"Ah! Would ye?" said the lion, and went at the boar in a rage.

"Is he dead?" asked Sep, when he came to himself.

"Oh, yes, he's *dead* right enough," said the lion; but the wind came up puffing and blowing, and said:

"It's no good, he's got away again, and now he's a fish. I was just a minute too late to see *what* fish!"

So then Sep went back to the palace, and he said to the King: "Let me marry the dear Princess and we'll go out and seek our fortune. I've got to kill that Magician, and I'll do it, too, or my name's not Septimus Septimusson. But it may take years and years, and I can't be away from the Princess all that time, because she won't eat unless I feed her. You see the difficulty, Sire?"

The King saw it. And that very day Sep was married to the Princess in her green gown with the red roses on it, and they set out together.

The wind went with them, and the wind, or something else, seemed to say to Sep, "Go home, take your wife home to your mother."

So he did. He crossed the land and the sea, and he went up the red-brick path to his father's cottage, and said: "Father, Mother, here's my wife."

They were so pleased to see him alive that they didn't notice the Princess at first, but when they did notice her, they wondered at her beautiful face and her beautiful gown. It wasn't till they had all settled down to supper and they noticed Sep feeding his wife as one feeds a baby, that they saw that she was blind.

And then all the story had to be told.

"Well, well," said the fisherman, "you and your wife bide here with us. I daresay I'll catch that old sinner in my nets one of these fine days." But he never did. And Sep and his wife lived with them. And they were happy after a fashion – but every evening, Sep used to wander and wonder by the seashore, wondering as he wandered whether he wouldn't ever have the luck to catch that fish.

And one evening he heard a little, sharp, thin voice say: "Sep, I've got it."

"What?" asked Sep.

"I've got it," said a big mussel on a rock close by him; "the magic stone that the Magician does his enchantments with. He dropped it out of his mouth and I shut my shells on it – and now he's sweeping up and down the sea like a mad fish, looking for it – for he knows he can never change into anything else unless he gets it back. Here, take the nasty thing; it's making me feel quite ill."

It opened its shells wide, and Sep saw a pearl. He reached out his hand and took it.

"That's better," said the mussel, washing its shells out with salt water.

"Can *I* do magic with it?" Sep eagerly asked.

"No," said the mussel sadly, "it's of no use to anyone but the owner. Now, if I were you, I'd get into a boat, and if your friend the wind will help us, I believe we really can do the trick."

"I'm at your service, of course," said the wind, getting up instantly.

The mussel whispered to the wind, who rushed off at once; and Sep launched his boat.

"Now," said the mussel, "you get into the very middle of the sea – or as near as you can guess it. The wind will warn all the other fishes." As he spoke he disappeared in the dark waters.

Sep got the boat into the middle of the sea – as near as he could guess it – and waited.

After a long time he saw something swirling about in a sort of whirlpool about a hundred yards from his boat, but, when he tried to move the boat towards it, her bow ran on to something hard.

"Keep still, keep still, keep still!" cried thousands and thousands of sharp, thin little voices. "You'll kill us if you move."

Then he looked over the boat side and saw that the hard something was nothing but thousands and thousands of mussels all jammed close together, and through the clear water more and more were coming and piling themselves together. Almost at once his boat was slowly lifted – the top of the mussel heap showed through the water, and ▶

there he was, high and dry on a mussel reef.

And in all that part of the sea the water was disappearing, and as far as the eye could see stretched a great plain of purple and grey – the shells of countless mussels. Only at one spot was there still a splashing.

Then a mussel opened its shell and spoke. Septimus bent forward to listen.

"We've got him," it said. "We've piled ourselves up till we've filled this part of the sea. The wind warned all the good fishes – and we got the old traitor in a little pool over there. Get out and walk over our backs – we'll all lie sideways so as not to hurt you. You must catch the fish – but, whatever you do, don't kill it till we give the word."

Sep promised, and he got out and walked over the mussels to the pool, and when he saw the wicked soul of the Magician looking out through the round eyes of a big finny fish, he remembered all that his Princess had suffered, and he longed to draw his sword and kill the wicked thing then and there. But he remembered the promise he had given the mussels. He threw a net about it, and dragged it back to the boat.

Then the mussels moved aside and let the boat down again into the water – and he rowed home, towing the evil fish in the net by a line.

He beached the boat and looked along the shore. The shore looked a very odd colour. And well it might, for every bit of the sand was covered with purple-grey mussels. They had all come up out of the sea – leaving just one little bit of real yellow sand for him to beach the boat on.

"Now," said millions of sharp, thin little voices, "kill him!"

Sep drew his sword and waded into the shallow surf and killed the evil fish

with one strong stroke. And at that, such a shout went up all along the shore as that shore had never heard; and all along the shore where the mussels had been stood men in armour and men in smock-frocks and men in leather aprons and huntsmen's coats and women and children – a whole nation of people. Close by the boat stood a King and Queen with crowns upon their heads.

"Thank you, Sep," said the King. "You've saved us all. I am the King Mussel, doomed to be a mussel so long as that wretch lived. You have set us all free. And look!"

Down the path from the shore came running his own Princess crying his name and looking at him with the most beautiful eyes in the world.

"Come!" said the Mussel King. "We have no son. You shall be our son and reign after us."

"Thank you," said Sep. "But *this* is my father," and he presented the old fisherman to His Majesty.

"Then let him come with us," said the King, royally. "He can help me reign, or fish in the palace lake, which-ever he prefers."

"Thank you," said Sep's father. "I think I'll come and fish."

"Your mother, too," said the Mussel Queen, kissing Sep's mother.

"Ah," said Sep's mother. "You're a lady, every inch. I'll go to the world's end with you."

So they all went back by way of the foreign country where Sep had found his Princess, and they called on the old lord. He had lost his ugly hump, and they persuaded him to come with them.

"You can help me reign if you like, or we have a nice book or two in the palace library," said the Mussel King.

"Thank you," said the old lord. "I'll come and be your librarian if I may. Reigning isn't at all in my line."

Then they went on to Sep's father-in-law, and when he saw how happy they all were together he said: "Bless my beard, but I've half a mind to come with you."

"Come along," said the Mussel King, "you shall help me reign if you like . . . or . . ."

"No, thank you," said the other King very quickly, "I've had enough of reigning. My kingdom can elect a President and be a republic if it likes. I'm going to look for butterflies."

And so he does, most happily, up to this very minute. *

Songs for Sevens

by Toni Arthur * Illustrated by Richard Hook

Toni Arthur travels all over the world, singing songs with and for children. Here are three especially for you.

Katie Beardie's Circus

Katie Beardie had a sheep,
She taught it well to skip and leap.
Wasn't that a clever sheep?
Good old Katie Beardie.

Chorus:
Clap, clap, clap your hands,
Clap your hands along with us.
Clap, clap, clap your hands,
Going to the circus.

Katie Beardie had a pig,
She taught it well to dance a jig.
Wasn't that a clever pig?
Good old Katie Beardie.

Katie Beardie had some mice,
She taught them well to skate on ice.
Weren't they all such clever mice?
Good old Katie Beardie.

Katie Beardie had a frog,
She taught it to dance on a wooden log.
Wasn't that a clever frog?
Good old Katie Beardie.

Katie Beardie had a snail,
She taught it to balance on a nail.
Wasn't that a clever snail?
Good old Katie Beardie.

Katie Beardie had a worm,
It could do a juggling turn,
Wasn't that a clever worm?
Good old Katie Beardie.

Katie Beardie had a hen,
It could count from one to ten,
Wasn't that a clever hen?
Good old Katie Beardie.

Dave and Toni Arthur

Today Is My Birthday

I woke up this morning with a tingle in my tum.
Something's very special and I know it will be fun.
Why won't all the world wake up, and see the day's begun?
For today is my birthday!

I've washed my face and cleaned my teeth
and even combed my hair.
What a lovely day it is, the sun shines everywhere.
And when I get to breakfast,
there are cards upon my chair.
For today is my birthday!

I feel I am much taller and I know I look just grand.
Someone came around and put a present in my hand.
Everyone is smiling, guess this must be fairyland.
For today is my birthday!

All my friends are coming here to share a party tea.
Jellies, ice-cream, games and fun, a special cake for me.
And all the world can see that I'm as happy as can be.
For today is my birthday!

What Can It Be?

Walk-ing a-long, creeping a-long, don't make a sound.

Look-ing a-round, what can it be, there on the ground?

Wig-gly worm or tiny vole, skylark's nest or velvet mole,

Many clues left in the earth, waiting to be found.

Walking along, creeping along, don't make a sound.
Looking around, what can it be, there on the ground?
Wiggly worm or tiny vole,
Skylark's nest or velvet mole,
Many clues left in the earth, waiting to be found.

Walking along, creeping along, move with a care.
Looking around, what can it be, there in the air?
Bumble bee or butterfly,
Moth and wasp all hurry by,
Busy buzzing, flitter fluttering, dashing everywhere.

Walking along, creeping along, mind you take care.
Looking around, what can it be, what's over there?
Frog or snail or slimy slug,
Bluebells, bear or ladybug,
Lots of living things around everywhere.

Here are two card games with a grown-up flavour.

Seven is the Number
Illustrated by Naomi Games

Sevens

Number of players: Three to eight. You'll need one pack of cards and buttons or chips to use as *counters*.

Dealing: One at a time until all the cards have been dealt. It doesn't matter if some players get more cards than others.

To win the game: Get rid of all your cards.

How to Play

Each player in turn, beginning with the player at the dealer's *left,* must play a card if possible. If that player cannot play a card, he or she must put a counter into the middle of the table. (**All** players should be given the same number of counters to begin a game.)

What cards to play: Any seven; or any card in the same suit and in sequence with a card previously played. For example, suppose that the player at the dealer's left puts the seven of spades down on the table. The next player may put down a *new* seven or he or she may play the eight (or six) of spades, so that it covers half of the seven of spades. If the eight of spades has been played, the next player has the right to put down the nine of spades. Once the nine of spades has been played, the next player has the right to put down the ten of spades, and so on.

At any turn, a player may put down a *new* seven or may continue a sequence that builds up from a seven to a King or down from a seven to an ace. The King is the highest card that may be played in a sequence and the ace is the lowest card that may be played in a sequence.

The play goes on until one person gets rid of all of his or her cards. That player then collects all the counters in the middle of the table. In addition, each loser pays to the winner one counter for each card left in his or her hand.

How to win the game: It's always a good idea to get rid of your very highest and very lowest cards as early as you can — then you can wait and play your middle-number cards at the end — and "go out."

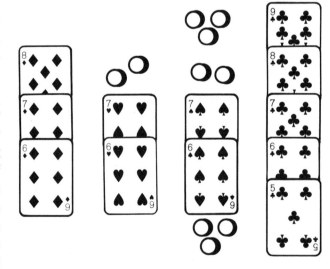

Klondike Solitaire

How to Play

1. From one pack deal a row of **seven** cards, the first (at left) face up and the others face down. These cards start your **seven** piles, which you can think of as numbered from one to **seven**, left to right.

2. Next, deal one card face up on pile *two,* and one card face down on each of the other piles from three to seven. Continue with a card face up on pile *three* and cards face down on piles four to seven. So, the first pile has just *one* card while the last — or seventh pile — has seven cards. The top card of each pile is face up and all the others are face down. The rest of the cards are left on the side, face down, as the *stock.*

3. You may move the face-up cards to build them onto each other. In building, you must alternate colours, red on black or black on red, and go down in number sequence. So, the four of clubs may be moved upon the five of hearts or on the five of diamonds. Kings are highest, and may be moved *only* into spaces created by removing piles.

4. In building, keep the cards spread *downward,* so that you can read them all. When two or more cards are built on each other, move all of them as a unit. [For example, if you have a black 10 on a red Jack, you may move the two cards together onto a black Queen.] Whenever you move a face-up card away from a pile, then you may turn up the next face-down card.

5. Aces are *base* cards. Whenever you have an ace on a pile [or turn an ace from your stock], put it down in a row *above* the piles. Build up on the aces in suit and number sequence: **A, 2, 3, 4, . . . J, Q, K.**

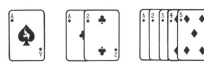

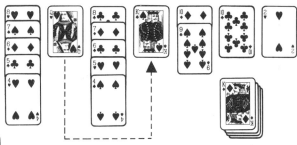

6. After you have done all the building you can onto the piles and aces (if any), turn over the top card of the remaining stock. Play this card on a pile or base if you can. If not, set it aside face up to start your waste pile. *You may go through the stock only once.*

How to win the game: you must get all four suits built up on the aces in four piles. You must put aces in the base row whenever they turn up, but you are not compelled to build on them when you can. It sometimes pays to keep cards on the piles, instead of moving them to bases, in order to help in building. ✳

Danger! Dragons and Worms is the cry!
Your task is to collect the three flags in the castle grounds. To do this you must travel through the tunnels, avoiding the giant pink Worms that will eat you up!

You will be helped on your way through the maze by seven trusty Dragons who point the way with their tails, showing you the best way into the castle grounds.

by Rowan Barnes-Murphy

Climb the towers and remove the flags, returning to the outside world — and safety!

MY SEVENTH BIRTHDAY, HURRAH!

by Franz Brandenberg
Illustrated by Aliki

"I'll be seven next Monday," said Alexa.
"That's old enough to run my birthday party
all by myself."
"Who will you invite?"
asked her brother, Jason.
"My whole class," said Alexa.

"Will there be any entertainment?" asked Father.
"I'll have a magic show," said Alexa.
"Oh, good!" said Father. "I'll start practising my tricks."
"Don't bother," said Alexa. "I am getting a real magician."
"What about games?" asked Jason.
"We'll play Pin-the-Tail-on-the-Donkey," said Alexa.
"I'll get you a tail from the toyshop," said Jason.
"No, thank you," said Alexa. "I'll make one myself."
"What will you serve?" asked Mother.
"Cake and ice-cream," said Alexa.
"If you need help, you know where to find me," said Mother.
"I know how to bake a cake," said Alexa.

"Will there be any going home presents?" asked Jason.
"I'll have balloons," said Alexa.
"Could I blow them up?" asked Jason.
"I told you I am doing this all by myself," said Alexa.
"I have a whole week."

On Monday,
Alexa wrote the invitations, and the letter to the magician.
"Shall I post them on the way to my piano lesson?" asked Jason.
"That would be a great help, thank you," said Alexa.
Jason put the letters into his book bag.

On Tuesday,
Alexa bought the balloons.

On Wednesday,
Alexa made the donkey's tail.

On Thursday,
Alexa bought the ice-cream.

On Friday,
Alexa ironed her party dress.

On Saturday,
Alexa decorated her room.

On Sunday,
Alexa baked the cake.
"It's a nice big cake," said Jason, "but a bit flat."
"Did you put in the baking powder?" asked Mother.
"You didn't tell me to," said Alexa.
"You didn't ask," said Mother.
"It doesn't matter," said Jason. "We'll just pile a lot
of ice-cream on top, and no one will notice."
"If you take it out of the freezer a little before you serve it,
it will be easy to scoop," said Mother.

▶

On Alexa's birthday,
the teacher gave her a surprise party.
"We didn't know it was your birthday," said her classmates.
"Are you having a home birthday party?"
"Yes, I am," said Alexa. "Right after school."
"Who is invited?" asked the children.
"All of you," said Alexa. "I sent out your invitations
a week ago!"
"We never got them," said the children.
"You are all invited now," said Alexa. "I hope you can come."

"They didn't bring you any presents," said Jason.
"They didn't have time to get any," said Alexa.
"They never received the invitations."
"No party hats?" asked Jason.
"I forgot to buy them," said Alexa.
"They're easy to make," said Mother.
She gave every one a sheet of coloured paper,
and showed them how.

"Where is the magician?" asked Jason.
"He let me down," said Alexa.
"No he didn't," said Father, dressed in his magician's costume.
Every one loved his magic show.

"Let's play Pin-the-Tail-on-the-Donkey," said Jason.
"I can't find the tail," said Alexa.
"What does it look like?" asked Jason.
"Like a piece of string," said Alexa.
"Like this one?" asked Jason, pointing at a string
tied around his book bag.

50

"That's it," said Alexa.
Jason untied the string, and the book bag fell open.
"Here are the invitations!" said Alexa.
"Oh, no! I forgot to post them," said Jason.
"That's why we didn't get them," said the children.
"And here is the letter to the magician!" said Alexa.
"That's why *he* didn't come."
"We didn't miss him," said the children.
"Your father was better than any real magician."

When they finished playing Pin-the-Tail-on-the-Donkey,
Jason brought out the cake.
"Where is the ice-cream?" asked Alexa.
"It's melted," said Jason.
"Mother told me to take it out of the freezer early,"
said Alexa.
"But not too early," said Mother.
"It doesn't matter," said Jason. "We can drink it,
like a milk shake."
"It tastes good out of a cup," said the children.

They sang, "Happy birthday to you,"
and Alexa blew out the seven candles.

It was time to go home.
"I forgot to blow up the balloons," said Alexa.
"We can all blow up our own," said Jason.
"That was a fun party," said the children.
"Thank you for inviting us!"
"I am glad you could come," said Alexa.
"We'll bring your presents to school tomorrow,"
said the children.
"That will be like another party," said Jason.
"Wow! Three parties for one birthday!" said Alexa.
"And you did it all alone," said Mother.
"Almost alone," said Alexa. "Thank you for your help."
"I think I'll run my tenth birthday party all by myself, too,"
said Jason.
"Can I bake the cake?" asked Alexa.
"If you don't forget the baking powder," said Jason.
"You know where to find us if you need help,"
said their parents. *

Let's Play a Game

by Deborah Manley and Peta Rée

Illustrated by David McKee

*Some good games for a birthday party —
or any rainy Saturday afternoon.*

Drawing Clumps

Each team has some pieces of paper and
a pencil and a table or board to rest the
paper on. The umpire has a list of
possible subjects — like a donkey eating
a carrot, a seagull, a daffodil, a cup of
coffee and so on. The first member of
each team comes up to the umpire, who
whispers one of the subjects in his or
her ear. He then rushes back to his team
and draws it. The other team members
try to guess what it is. They may only
ask, "Is it a . . .?" and the artist may only
answer "Yes" or "No". When the team
guesses correctly, the next member
rushes to the umpire, whispers the
answer and is given a new object to
draw. The team which guesses all the
things on the list first wins.

The game can be made more difficult
if the list includes activities rather than
objects: a girl playing croquet, a man
mowing the lawn, a dog jumping
through a hoop or a cow jumping over
the moon.

Or the teams could draw and guess
proverbs: "a stitch in time saves nine",
"a rolling stone gathers no moss", "the
early bird catches the worm", and so on.
Or they could draw and guess nursery
rhymes: "Humpty Dumpty", "Mary Had a
Little Lamb", or "Hickory Dickory Dock".

*

As Bright as a Button

This game can be played by individuals,
but it is probably better to pool your
knowledge and work as a team.

There are a large number of phrases —
or clichés — like the one that gives its
name to this game. The teams have to
guess the phrases you have in mind
from the clues you give them.

You will need cards with numbers on
them, one for each phrase; a variety of
objects to use as clues; and pencils and
paper for the teams. Scatter the cards
about the room and place one clue
object on each. The cards should be far
enough apart so that one team won't be
able to overhear the conversation of the
other!

At a signal, the teams have to look at
the clues and decide what phrases they
represent and write down the answer
against the card number on their paper.
The team with the most correct answers
within a given time wins.

A game might go like this:

Clues	Answers
A button	As bright as a button

(Use this as an example to explain the
game.)

A feather	As light as a feather
A piece of brass	As bold as brass
A whistle	As clean as a whistle
Two sticks	As cross as two sticks
A pin	As neat as a pin
A picture	As pretty as a picture
A cricket bat	As blind as a bat
Some soot	As black as soot
A piece of silk	As soft as silk

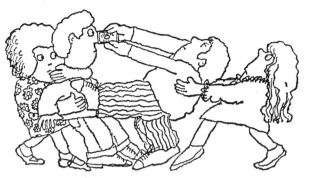

Pass the Matchbox

For this contest you need two ordinary matchboxes and two teams of children. The teams stand in line one behind the other. A matchbox cover is placed on the nose of the first child in each line. They turn around and place their matchboxes on to the noses of the people behind them — *without using their hands*. The matchboxes continue on down the line. Remember, you mustn't use your hands to assist you. The last person runs with the matchbox still on his nose up to the umpire. If the matchbox is dropped *at any point* it must be passed back to the first person to begin its journey down the line of noses once again!

Happy playing! *

As thick as thieves

The Seven Wonders of the World
by Tania Cooke * Illustrated by Daniel Woods

In the reign of Alexander the Great — who conquered all Greece and the huge Kingdom of Persia over 300 years before Jesus was born (B.C.) — Greeks began to travel without the fear of being robbed and killed. But what should they visit? Even then, travellers needed some kind of a guide book. The very first such guide was a list made by the Greeks in the 3rd Century B.C. It was a list of seven famous things created by man. They were called the "Seven Wonders of the World".

When the Greek travellers sailed across the Mediterranean Sea to Egypt, how did they know they had arrived? They knew because a wonderful light shone out upon the sea, from the first of the seven wonders, the *Lighthouse of Alexandria.*

Rising above the ancient city of Alexandria, it was the tallest tower in the world, finished in 280 B.C. after nineteen years of building. At its top burned a huge fire day and night which was fed with a supply of pine logs dragged by mules up a spiral pathway in the tower. Behind the fire stood an enormous sheet of polished bronze, so that the fire was reflected out to sea. On the very top was a statue of Poseidon, the Greek god of the sea. It was unlike any other lighthouse in the world. ▶

The travellers then crossed a hundred miles of desert to the second wonder, the *Great Pyramid of Egypt*. It was, even then, an ancient tomb made for a great King, half-buried in the sand and already over 2,000 years old when the Greeks visited it. And it was huge — over 147 metres high and each side of the base was 230 metres long. For nearly 5,000 years it was the biggest building in the world. Far away it looked like a pointed hill above the desert, with polished sides and a gold top shining in the sun. Even now we only *think* we know how it was built — hundreds of slaves dragging over two million blocks of stone uphill into position.

Alexandria

Giza

The Lighthouse at Alexandria

The Great Pyramid

The Hanging Gardens

Leaving the pyramid they began on a long, difficult journey to the *Hanging Gardens of Babylon,* stopping at wells and oases for water for their camels. But the long journey was part of the wonder. At Babylon — the largest city in the world — they went through tall towers guarded by lions in the moat below. Before them was a splendid highway leading to the Gardens themselves. Built about 600 B.C. by King Nebuchadnezzar, they were already three hundred years old when the lighthouse was built at Alexandria. A huge pyramid of trees, shrubs and flowers from all over the world rose a hundred feet above the centre of the city. The trees and flowers grew so thickly that they hid the buildings behind. How were they watered in that very hot country? — probably by slaves working a treadmill carrying buckets of water to the top.

Babylon

54

The party of Greek tourists then journeyed back to the coast and by ship to the island of Rhodes. From afar they saw their fourth wonder, the tallest statue in the world, called the *Colossus of Rhodes*. This great shining bronze statue of a naked god looking out to sea was over 30 metres tall (eighteen times human size) and was finished in 280 B.C. He had one hand raised to his eyes to direct the sunbeams out across the sea, and, in his other hand, he held a cloak to sweep the darkness from the sky each morning. On his head he wore a crown of spiky sun-like rays. He must have shone brightly in the sunshine and been reflected from the glittering surface of the sea. Alas, he only stood for fifty-six years before an earthquake toppled him over, but then he lay for more than nine hundred years on the ground. I wonder which the travellers saw?

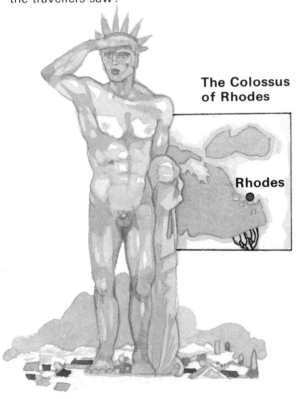

The Colossus of Rhodes

Rhodes

From Rhodes the travellers sailed north, along the coast to the harbour of Halicarnassus. From there they could see the fifth wonder, another giant tomb, called *The Mausoleum* because it was designed for King Mausolus and his Queen Artemisia. It was 42.6 metres high and was made in three parts, a huge base, more than 9 metres square and made of solid marble, with a pillared temple above, and –

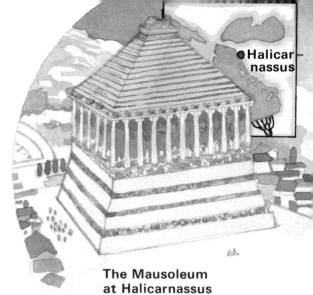

Halicarnassus

The Mausoleum at Halicarnassus

on top of that a huge pyramid with a statue of a chariot pulled by four horses. The tomb, finished in 350 B.C., stood above the harbour, with houses squeezed round on little stepped streets. As they came closer they could see the real wonder; its stone work decorated with beautiful statues and carvings of battles, painted and polished and shining in the sunlight.

Further up the coast was the *Temple at Ephesus,* the biggest in the world, longer and broader than the Mausoleum and 30 metres high. The temple had a mysterious beginning: a piece of meteorite – something like a shooting star – fell out of the sky more than 3,000 years ago and killed a king. The people kept the meteorite, which was a huge stone shaped like a human being and covered in bumps like a fircone. They believed it was the goddess, Mother Earth. First it was worshipped in a temple built of mud. Then a rich king built a large temple, and, finally, Alexander the Great rebuilt it even more magnificently. Every part of the temple – with its 127 pillars – was decorated with carvings and richly-coloured paintings. It remained one of the wonders of the world for 500 years.

The Temple at Ephesus ▶

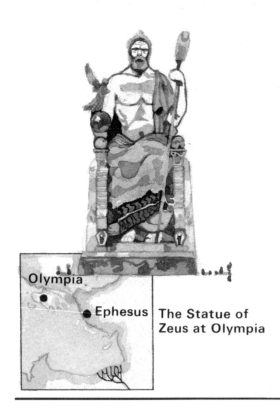

Going home from Ephesus the travellers sailed across the Aegean Sea, and along the coast of Greece until they could land at a harbour and take a mule or donkey along the narrow mountain roads to the magnificent *Temple of Zeus at Olympia*. It was 64 metres by 27 metres and inside was a beautiful statue of Zeus, seven times as tall as a man. It was made by the most famous sculptor in Greece, Phidias, out of wonderful materials — sheets of ivory for his body with golden robes and sandals, and covered with jewels. Even his great throne was painted and carved and studded with precious stones. It was completed in 430 B.C. and stood for 800 years and the people were so frightened of the god that nothing was ever stolen from it.

When they returned home, the travellers would tell others about their wonderful journey — and more people would then set out to visit the Seven Wonders of the World. ✳

Olympia

Ephesus | **The Statue of Zeus at Olympia**

7... 17... 27... Who and What?
by Deborah Manley

Famous people and events associated with the number seven.

Have you heard of **Benjamin Franklin, Lewis Carroll** or **Charles Dickens**? Or maybe you're familiar with **Davy Crockett** or **Mozart**?

Why do I ask? Well, all of them are linked to the number seven. Some were born on the 7th — or 17th or 27th — day of a month. Some did great deeds on those days. They are all "sevens people." Some great occasions are linked to seven too. Read on and find out how!

Malch 17th is **St Patrick's** Day. He is the patron saint of Ireland. He was taken as a slave to Ireland but escaped. Later he returned there to teach the people of Ireland about Christianity. It is believed that he banished all snakes from Ireland forever. St Patrick died about 460 AD.

Benjamin Franklin, while flying his kite, made an electrifying discovery!

Benjamin Franklin was born in Boston on 17 January 1706. He lived in Philadelphia. There he founded its first public library, first fire service and first hospital. He became famous as a statesman, printer and writer, and was interested in everything! He helped to write the Declaration of Independence which was signed in Philadelphia on 17 September 1776. After a famous kite-flying incident, Franklin also in-

Charles Dickens, who created a host of unforgettable characters.

vented the lightning conductor — a metal rod that takes lightning into the ground without doing any harm. Most buildings have lightning conductors on them today.

Wolfgang Amadeus Mozart was born on 27 January 1756. By the time he was seven he had composed music and had played before the Austrian Empress at her palace in Vienna. He composed about 700 musical works in his lifetime.

Mozart, aged 7, playing the piano for the Empress of Austria.

On 7 October 1769 **Captain James Cook** became the first European to visit the islands of New Zealand. He was an explorer who made three voyages to the Pacific Ocean and sailed around the world twice. In April 1770, he sailed into Botany Bay in Australia and claimed the land for Britain.

The "King of the Wild Frontier" — **Davy Crockett** — was born on 17 August 1786 in Greene County, Tennessee. He became a famous woodsman, hunter, legislator and Indian fighter. People loved to tell "tall stories" about Davy's adventures. He was a real-life comic book hero. He died in 1836, defending the Alamo in San Antonio, Texas.

The great writer, **Charles Dickens**, was born on 7 February 1812 at Portsmouth, England. He wrote many stories we still love today. Among them are *A Christmas Carol, Oliver Twist* and *David Copperfield.*

On 17 December 1903 the first person ever to fly an aeroplane took off. **Orville** and **Wilbur Wright** fitted an engine to a glider. On this day on the sand dunes of Kittyhawk in North Carolina, Orville made four flights. The longest was only 259 metres, but marked the first time that *anyone* had flown a heavier-than-air, power-driven machine, and the days of flying had begun.

A man called Charles Dodgson was born on 27 January 1832. He used another name to write books. It was **Lewis Carroll**. His books *Alice's Adventures in Wonderland* and *Alice Through the Looking Glass* are still read by children all around the world.

In *Through the Looking Glass,* Alice was seven years old. Seven years and six months old, as she told Humpty Dumpty when they met:

"Seven years and six months!" Humpty Dumpty repeated thoughtfully, "An uncomfortable sort of age. Now if you'd asked *my* advice, I'd have said 'Leave off at seven' . . . but it's too late now." ✳

Captain Cook sets foot on Botany Bay for the first time.

7 DEADLY SINS

by Anni Axworthy

In olden times, people were very careful to avoid the Seven Deadly Sins:
Gluttony, Pride, Sloth, Lust, Wrath, Envy and Avarice. Here are Seven Sins
which good sevens ought to avoid . . . if they can!

Noisiness

Pet-tiness

Aggressiveness

Greediness

Bad-temperedness

Clumsiness

Filthiness

Seven Days of the Week

*

by Peter Eldin * Illustrated by Kate Shannon

You know, of course, that there are seven days in a week. But have you ever wondered *why* there are seven days and why they have such unusual names?

The most likely reason for there being seven days in a week is because people in olden times thought there were seven planets going around the sun – we now know there are really nine! Some of the English names for the days of the week actually come from the names of planets: Sunday is the day of the sun (except when it rains!); Monday is the day of the Moon; and Saturday is the day of Saturn.

The four other days of the week are named after the gods of the Norsemen who lived in Scandinavia. Tuesday is the day of Tiw, the god of war; Wednesday is the day of Wodin (or Odin), ruler of the gods; Thursday is the day of Thor, the god of thunder; and Friday is the day of Frigga, who was the wife of Wodin.

Riddles

What seven-letter name has only three letters?

Barbara.

What seven-letter word still has seven left when you've taken two letters away?

Seventy.

If you had seven cows and seven goats, what would you have?

Plenty of milk.

Seven men took seven hours to dig a hole. How long would it take them to dig half a hole?

* No one can dig *half* a hole!

The Magpie's Nest

Retold by Treld Bicknell ● Illustrated by Charles Front

*A curious tale of seven birds and seven nests –
from the Piegan Indians of the Northern forests.*

When the people of the Indian nations first built their wigwams in the forests, all the animals came to look at them. How interesting they were to the wolf and the bear and the wildcat! They had strong walls to keep out the wind and rain, and cozy fires which burned brightly within. But these wonderful wigwams were even more interesting to the birds – for each one of them was different from all the others.

The birds gathered round, twittering and cawing with excitement. They decided that they, too, should build such beautiful homes for themselves. Then the eagle (who was chieftain of all the birds) commanded that each bird should begin at once to build a suitable home for itself.

The birds set to work and each bird's nest was a true expression of its nature. The woodpecker hammered a home out of the trunk of a stout tree with his strong sharp beak, and the swallows carefully fashioned mounds of mud and waited patiently for them to dry. The crows searched among the leaves for just the right twigs with which to build their tree-top homes. Down below, the tiny hummingbird worked hardest of all, decorating her finished nest with patterns of fresh, green moss.

But not all the birds were so hard-working – some were careless and lazy. The owl simply chose a hollow in a nearby tree and filled it with a few leaves before settling down to rest. The plump partridge hollowed a little spot for herself in the grass in her good-natured way and waited for it to grow up around her. And the sociable, gossiping magpie? Why, she did nothing at all! She hated work and loved to chatter, flitting from place to place – ever curious, ever restless. "I don't know *how* to build," she declared, "and there are always branches to rest on at night."

Soon all the birds – except the magpie – had finished with their work. Then the Great Spirit came to them, saying: "You have done well, my children, and I will reward you." With that, he pulled from his huge head-dress four white eagles' feathers and, giving one each to the East Wind, West Wind, South Wind and North Wind, he said: "Take these feathers and blow across all the lands until sunrise tomorrow, and fill every nest you pass with eggs. . . ."

The winds billowed and rose, carrying the four feathers to the four corners of the earth. And, as they blew over the forests, they filled the waiting nests with eggs – cream, white, grey, speckled and delicate blue – the right colour for each nest. And a new generation of birds was ready to be born.

The birds were all happy, all except the magpie. She grew more and more unhappy as the kindly winds blew. She tried desperately to scrape together a nest so that she, too, could share in the ▶

gift from the Great Spirit. But she did not know how. She rushed here and there, begging the other birds for help. The woodpecker gave her a few splinters, and the crows some carefully-chosen twigs. She begged grasses from the partridge, moss from the hummingbird and a little mud from the swallows. Carrying everything to the top of a tall pine tree, she flung the bits together to make a nest – just before the wind carried the Great Spirit's white feather to her tree-top.

When the sun rose, all the birds left their nests and called to one another throughout the forest. Each bird wanted to tell all the others about its beautiful eggs. All but the magpie – she was nowhere to be seen. So the other birds flocked to the tall pine tree. There they found the magpie in the oddest and most untidy nest they had ever seen.

Angrily she fluttered around and around the nest exclaiming: "One, two, three, four. . . . NO, only three! Oh, how can I count them like this!" And all the birds understood at once – the magpie was trying in vain to count the eggs hidden in that messy nest.

The eagle spoke: "If you had not been so lazy and careless and had built a *proper* nest, you could now be content with your gift from the Great Spirit." Then the eagle turned and flew away from the protesting magpie, and the whole bird nation followed him.

And that is why, to this day, the magpie's nest is the ugliest and most untidy in all the forest – and why she never knows how many eggs she has been given by the Great Spirit. ✳